The Ballad of William Sycamore
(1790-1871)

THE BALLAD
of
WILLIAM SYCAMORE

(*1790-1871*)

by
Stephen Vincent Benét

Illustrated by
Brinton Turkle

Little, Brown and Company
BOSTON   **TORONTO**

The text of "The Ballad of William Sycamore" has been reprinted from *Ballads and Poems* by Stephen Vincent Benét. This edition has been published by special arrangement with Holt, Rinehart, and Winston, Inc.

*Published simultaneously in Canada
by Little, Brown & Company (Canada) Limited*

PRINTED IN THE UNITED STATES OF AMERICA

The Ballad of William Sycamore
(1790-1871)

My father, he was a mountaineer,

His fist was a knotty hammer;

He was quick on his feet as a running deer,

And he spoke with a Yankee stammer.

My mother, she was merry and brave,

And so she came to her labor,

With a tall green fir for her doctor grave

And a stream for her comforting neighbor.

8

And some are wrapped in the linen fine,

And some like a godling's scion;

But I was cradled on twigs of pine

In the skin of a mountain lion.

And some remember a white, starched lap

And a ewer with silver handles;

But I remember a coonskin cap

And the smell of bayberry candles.

The cabin logs, with the bark still rough,

And my mother who laughed at trifles,

And the tall, lank visitors, brown as snuff,

With their long, straight squirrel-rifles.

I can hear them dance, like a foggy song,

Through the deepest one of my slumbers,

The fiddle squeaking the boots along

And my father calling the numbers.

The quick feet shaking the puncheon-floor,

And the fiddle squealing and squealing,

Till the dried herbs rattled above the door

And the dust went up to the ceiling.

There are children lucky from dawn till dusk,

But never a child so lucky!

For I cut my teeth on "Money Musk"

In the Bloody Ground of Kentucky!

When I grew tall as the Indian corn,

My father had little to lend me,

But he gave me his great, old powder-horn

And his woodsman's skill to befriend me.

With a leather shirt to cover my back,

And a redskin nose to unravel

Each forest sign, I carried my pack

As far as a scout could travel.

Till I lost my boyhood and found my wife,

A girl like a Salem clipper!

A woman straight as a hunting-knife

With eyes as bright as the Dipper!

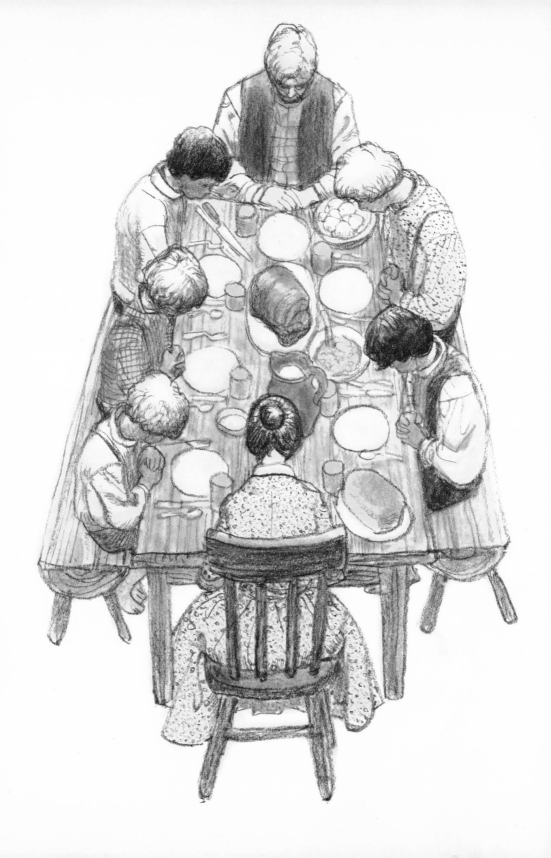

We cleared our camp where the buffalo feed,

Unheard-of streams were our flagons;

And I sowed my sons like the apple-seed

On the trail of the Western wagons.

They were right, tight boys, never sulky or slow,

A fruitful, a goodly muster.

The eldest died at the Alamo.

The youngest fell with Custer.

The letter that told it burned my hand.

Yet we smiled and said, "So be it!"

But I could not live when they fenced the land,

For it broke my heart to see it.

I saddled a red, unbroken colt

And rode him into the day there;

And he threw me down like a thunderbolt

And rolled on me as I lay there.

The hunter's whistle hummed in my ear

As the city-men tried to move me,

And I died in my boots like a pioneer

With the whole wide sky above me.

Now I lie in the heart of the fat, black soil,

Like the seed of a prairie-thistle;

It has washed my bones with honey and oil

And picked them clean as a whistle.

And my youth returns, like the rains of Spring,

And my sons, like the wild-geese flying;

And I lie and hear the meadow-lark sing

And have much content in my dying.

Go play with the towns you have built of blocks,

The towns where you would have bound me!

I sleep in my earth like a tired fox,

And my buffalo have found me.